Golfing Gags from Silvey-Jex

Published in the UK by
POWERFRESH Limited
Unit 3 Everdon Park
Heartlands Business Park
Daventry
NN11 8YJ

Telephone 01327 871 777
Facsimile 01327 879 222
E Mail   info@powerfresh.co.uk

Copyright :   © 2006 The Silvey & Jex Partnership
                Cover and interior layout by Powerfresh

ISBN 10: 1904967558
ISBN 13: 9781904967552

Printed in Malta by Gutenberg Press limited

TRY AND REMEMBER THE BASKET BEFORE YOU PRESS THE BUTTON
BALL MACHINE
DRIVING RANGE
SILVEY-JEX

WHERE DID YOU GET THAT CLUB- THE PRO SHOP OR THE TOYSHOP?
SILVEY-JEX

HOW COULD HE HEAR YOU SHOUT "FORE" WHEN HE'S ON HIS MOBILE
SILVEY-JEX

WHY IS IT WHENEVER I HIT A GOOD LONG DRIVE IT ALWAYS GOES IN THE OTHER DIRECTION?
350 YDS. PAR 4
NEY JEX